The Supernatural Spine

by

Dr. Roy J. Le Roy
Norma Jean Le Roy

Published by
Hunter Books
P.O. BOX 5600
Kingwood, TX 77325-5600

Books and Tapes By
Dr. Roy J. Le Roy
and
Norma Jean Le Roy
Impossible Miracles Ministry
549 Manor Drive, N.E.
Minneapolis, MN 55432

Video Tapes:
Ministering Healing (2 Hours)
The Crucifixion (From A Doctor's Viewpoint) (1 Hour)

Audio Tapes:
Ministering Healing To Yourself (1/2 Hour)
My Testimony: Norma Jean Le Roy (1 Hour)
Unforgiveness: A Hindrance To Healing (1 Hour)

Books:
The Supernatural Spine
Impossible Miracles
(The story of Norma Jean Le Roy's healing)
by Charles & Frances Hunter

Published by Hunter Books

ISBN # 1-878209-09-4

Scripture quotations from:
The Authorized King James Version unless otherwise noted
The Amplified Bible, Expanded Edition (Amp) ©1987 by The Zondervan Corporation and The Lockman Foundation

Contents

Acknowledgments

Naturally, we are so very thankful that God has always had His hand on our lives, and given us years of experience, education and healing in preparation for our ministry. We are so grateful to all our friends and loved ones who have encouraged us in our ministry. Without your prayers and support, we would not have contemplated writing this book. We are deeply grateful to Charles and Frances Hunter, who are not only our very dear friends, but who have continually encouraged and supported us in our ministry. Also, we wish to especially thank Michelle Goins, without whose help this book would not have come into existence. Michelle spent many hours transcribing our tapes and compiling the information. We are very grateful to Carol Leo and Joan Knochel for sharing their artistic gifts. Carol drew the spine, skull, pelvic and posture diagrams and Joan did the exercise drawings. Our dear friend and professional photographer, Bill Conner, who has gone on home to the Lord, had blessed us with many of the pictures and we wish also to acknowledge our thanks and remembrance of Bill.

The Supernatural Spine

Foreword

To have friends who stay close to your heart year after year is a gift from God.

We consider Dr. Roy J. Le Roy and Norma Jean Le Roy to be constantly close to our hearts because of their special love for God and Christ Jesus, their complete dedication to Them and to each other, and for their love of doing Jesus' last instructions while He was on earth..."Lay hands on the sick, and they shall recover."

Norma Jean worked closely with us while Wally was alive; she worked closely with us as a widow; and her love continued as she and Doc became one in marriage.

Doc was new to us, but there was an instant bonding of our spirits, and we became a team of four, learning and doing what Jesus told all of us to do.

Doc has been invaluable in our learning how to minister healing. He purchased our book and devoured it day after day; at first skeptical, then when he tried to discover what was wrong professionally, there was nothing he could find. By that, he knew that only God could have given this powerful healing tool to the Body of Christ through two ordinary human beings.

Doc and Norma Jean worked closely with us for about six years of giant Healing Explosions, helping us train believers how to dispense God's Holy Spirit power in Jesus' Name into sick bodies and see them healed. The percentage and magnitude of miracles has vastly increased until today perhaps millions are daily ministering healing, just as Jesus said we believers would do.

Through the video tapes around the world, Doc and Norma Jean are known and loved wherever we go. And now they have written this book on the supernatural spine which will bless ever person interested in healing the sick.

The Le Roys are very precious in the kingdom of God, and loved and respected by all who come in contact with them and their ministry. They are precious and special in our lives.

Charles and Frances Hunter

Introduction

How we live influences our health. Some people exercise, jog or do other things to get in shape. Dr. Le Roy has devised a system using Charles and Frances Hunter's methods to heal the sick as a guide. For the past several years, Dr. Roy J. Le Roy and Norma Jean Le Roy have been sharing their testimonies. The knowledge Dr. Le Roy has of the body, and his experience in laying on hands and taking authority over the works of the devil using the Name of Jesus, in the power of the Holy Spirit, to minister healing are truly a wealth of information.

One day while Dr. Le Roy was praying, the Lord said to him, "Why don't you put on an audio tape how to minister healing to yourself?" After doing this and sharing the teaching with so many people, it has been requested that Dr. Le Roy share this teaching in a book. I have been blessed with the opportunity to compile the teachings, testimonies and audio tapes of Dr. Le Roy and Norma Jean, and I join the Le Roy's in prayer that the anointing of God will be upon this book; that He will bless each reader; and that the information contained herein will edify and encourage you in ministering healing to yourself and others.

Michelle Goins

CHAPTER ONE

Getting To Know Dr. Le Roy

So many of God's children want to learn how to minister to those who need healing. They go to various seminars and training sessions to be equipped to serve God in this area. Some received the "gifts of healing" from the Lord, while others, like myself, just desire to be vessels through which the Lord heals. Let me introduce myself to those who do not already know me. I am Dr. Roy J. Le Roy, a retired chiropractor with over 40 years' experience in chiropractorally laying on hands.

When I was a young man, I suffered from back trouble, sinus problems and bursitis. Seeking help for myself, I noticed in the local paper an ad placed by a chiropractor. The ad showed a picture of the spine with the nerves coming out and going to various parts of the body. The ad explained how adjusting the spine would help various physical conditions. I was fascinated by this and decided to learn the chiropractic profession.

I went to the National College in Chicago and upon graduation, I was licensed to practice in the state of Wisconsin. I did post-graduate work in sacro-occipital technique (which is a study of the function of the sacrum together with the occiput-the bottom and top of the spinal column). I studied under Dr. M.B. De Jarnette of Nebraska City, Nebraska. Dr. De Jarnette was one of the foremost research chiropractors in the country. He was a genius.

I had such a great desire to see people healed that I attended seminars twice a year since 1957 and I read, studied and literally devoured any information that I could get on the spine. I practiced for forty years in Green Bay, Wisconsin. As the world would measure success, I was doing quite well.

I had a lovely wife, Florence, children and opportunities to go to Europe six times, to the Holy Land, Africa, South America, Hawaii, Mexico and Canada. Yet, something was still missing in my life and I was not satisfied.

My search led me to the Lord. I began changing, was delivered from cursing, and experienced a peace I had never known before. I began reading the Bible and praying. I gave my heart to the Lord. Seeking to know all about Him, I just could not get enough of spiritual things. I attended meetings, conventions, Bible studies and received the Baptism with the Holy Spirit. After receiving the Baptism with the Holy Spirit, I found that I could work all day long without getting tired because the power of the Holy Spirit was flowing through me. People said they could feel something going through them when I laid hands on them. I found that, at times, I would not even have to give an adjustment because the Lord had already done the work. We get the blessings and God gets the glory!

While attending the Institute of Ministry in Bradenton, Florida, my wife, Florence, on March 6, 1982, after a series of heart attacks, went home to be with Jesus. What a devastating experience after 48 years of marriage to be suddenly left alone. I was 72 years old and in a state of shock and grief.

Back in 1980, being financially successful and looking for information to help get people healed, we had bought

5

the book "How To Heal The Sick" by Charles and Frances Hunter. During my period of grieving, I began studying this book and listening to the audio tapes on "How To Heal The Sick" during my lunch break from my practice each noon. I don't know how many times I played those tapes or read the book. It was so intriguing that it helped me to get over my grief. It was through studying this book that I realized what power we have over Satan and that he knows it. Satan also knows whether or not we know we have power over him. I realized what a tremendous gift we have.

Being a chiropractor, I knew what caused a short leg or arm and how to correct it by manipulation. I questioned Charles Hunter of the Happy Hunters' Ministry on how he learned to grow out arms and legs and he said that the Lord had revealed it to him.

It took Dr. De Jarnette twenty years to find out how to adjust both sides of the pelvis at the same time. Adjusting legs or arms took me years to learn, and after forty years of being a chiropractor, I found out that Jesus can adjust the body by me just giving a command in His name.

From this time on, I went to prayer meetings, prisons and hospitals to pray with anyone who would hold still. What a tremendous feeling when you know that you know that you know you are in God's will.

I continued to return to Bradenton to be in the Pastoral Training School. It was there that I met a gorgeous hunk of feminine pulchritude, an evangelist, Reverend Norma Jean Van Dell, who was a widow, and who was to change my life.

Getting To Know Norma Jean

Many who read this book may already know me or know about me, as much of my testimony of the wonderful healing I received from God on December 7, 1973, through the ministry of Charles and Frances Hunter has been shared in their book "Impossible Miracles." I was healed of disorders of the spine, skin, hair and various internal disorders. I was made whole by one touch from the Master.

For those who are not familiar with my testimony, in January of 1955 a truck ran into the back of my car causing an injury to my back. A disc slipped out into the spinal canal and ruptured (herniated). This swelling pressed on a nerve causing severe pain from my back, through my hip, down the back of my leg and into my toes. The surgery to correct this involved a laminectomy and a spinal fusion, which means they took the disc out and fused the space with bone from my hip. When they ran out of the bone in the hip, they used pelvic bone. The result of this was that they took three times as much bone from my hip as was recommended, thus making it impossible for me to walk alone and I required a wheelchair when going out. I had anywhere from one to three fusions at a time during six different spine operations.

Prior to the surgery, I was put through many extremely painful spinal tests. This was only the start of a series of events and operations. Between 1955 and 1973 I was in two automobile accidents. I had a total of ten operations (my body had become the surgeon's practice field) and 31 hospitalizations. Between 1962 and 1973, I was in constant pain. I almost died in the last operation and never recovered enough to function. I also had an electric hospital bed in my home. Other sicknesses began to occur. By 1967 I was losing my hair and by 1969 I was totally disabled. By 1972, it seemed like everything in my body went wrong.

My potassium went down, my kidneys, thyroid and bladder malfunctioned. Almost all of my hair was gone and my skin began flaking off. By now, I was unable to bend and wore a heavy steel brace for my spine. My hips were so hollow to provide bone in my spine and I would fall unless I was in a wheelchair or someone held onto me. I doubted if I would ever walk again. After twelve discouraging and agonizing years, never without pain, I was daily taking pain pills every three to four hours and two to four sleeping pills each night.

I thought the reason I couldn't be healed was because I figured the Lord could heal easy things. I didn't think He could get the bone that they had taken out of hips and put into my spine back into my hips. As I mentioned before, I had to either walk with help or go in a wheelchair because my hips were hollow.

I couldn't imagine that, since my spine and neck were held together with a screw and nail and I wore a steel brace, the Lord could get those bones out of my spine and back into my hips and get the screw and nail out through my flesh. However, on December 7, 1973 (most people call it "Pearl Harbor Day"--I call it "Norma Jean Day") my friends dragged me to that Hunter meeting at

Augsburg College. My friends insisted that I go to this Hunter meeting, which I thought was for deer hunters because that's what you do at that time of year in Minnesota. I went there against my will (I want to tell you that). My friend asked what did I care how the Lord does it as long as He does it? Well, I thought, there's no way to get out of this.

It was two below zero, not counting the wind chill, but I went and sat halfway down the room, figuring if there's anything to get I only had halfway to go up to get it. I thought I'd go up front and get it, and if it's too scary, then I would only have halfway to bug out. (I couldn't run out!).

At the time I went to this meeting, I was bald and wearing a wig and, as I mentioned before, my skin was all flaking off and my organs were failing. My kidneys had failed, bringing me close to death, my bladder wasn't working right and all my chemical balances were imbalanced.

At one time, I was told I would not live past the age of 35 (today I am way past that age and still living and serving God to the best of my ability).

Well, praise the Lord, I was healed!

People were falling to the ground when they were prayed for and I thought Charles Hunter was knocking them down. I also thought, He had better not knock me down because I had already paid enough hospital bills to put the air conditioning in Mt. Sinai Hospital and build a new wing!

When he prayed for me, it was like heat went all the way down my spine and spread out to each side, you know, like an electric blanket--which you need in Minnesota in the winter!

When the Hunters wrote the book, "Impossible Miracles," Charles wanted to verify that those bones were back in my hips since I was no longer falling. I couldn't even lean over to get a glass of water off the table and yet, after that healing I received when they prayed for me, I could bend down.

When they x-rayed me for the book, every fusion was still in there, my hips were still hollow, and the screw and the nail were still in my neck. I was still solidly fused, no more bendable than a steel pole, and yet I could bend.

So, it really doesn't matter if those hips are hollow, or if anything is back in place as long as it's healed. God can do it His way, so we shouldn't try to put God in a box.

Praise God, I was healed! That's all I really care about.

God still heals. He set me free from pain and suffering, caused my hair to grow back thick, beautiful and perfectly styled, and healed my skin problems and my back so I can bend, walk and live a normal life.

As a result of God healing me and freeing my husband, Wally Van Dell, from bondages at the same time, our marriage, which had been so strained due to the suffering, hardships and financial burdens, was also healed.

For many years, we went into ministry as traveling evangelists. On Sunday morning, June 28, 1981, the day after my 53rd birthday, Wally went home to be with Jesus after suffering from cancer.

I continued with the ministry, still traveling, pulling a trailer around the country, by the grace of God, without even knowing how to back it up. My friends began praying that God would send me a husband. Even Frances Hunter prayed for me to get a tall, dark, handsome, rich and spiritual husband.

I wasn't sure this was God's will for me so I only asked God to bring him across my path if He wanted me to have a husband. I even told God I wouldn't chase one down. Maybe I'd trip him, but not chase him down. Also, I had asked God to give me a specific signal so I would

10

know if it was the right one as I did not want to be hurt and surely did not want to be out of the will of God. I wanted what God had for me and nothing else.

One day after a church service in Florida, I looked toward the door of the church and there was Dr. Le Roy standing in the doorway.

I said, "Oh, Doc (as he is affectionately called) is back," and the signal went off. I said, "God, You've got to be kidding," because I knew he was older than I was and I had intended to marry someone about ten years younger than I was if I ever married so I wouldn't have to go through the death of a husband again.

Anyhow, I skipped over and gave Dr. Le Roy a hug as we all do at that church and the signal went off again and I just said, "Lord, I sure hope You know what You are doing," because I knew then that he was a dead duck. It took him three days before he knew it. This was January 28, 1984.

A New Ministry Team

On the date of March 11, 1984, Dr. Le Roy and I were united in marriage and a new ministry team was born. In case any of you wonder why God would bring two people with eighteen-and-a-half-years age difference together, Dr. Le Roy says, "I married a woman so much younger because I'd rather smell perfume than linament." Seriously, though, we know that when we trust in the Lord with all our heart; and lean not unto our own understanding and acknowledge Him in all our ways, He will direct our paths (see Proverbs 3:5). Dr. Le Roy is rich in spiritual gifts which I really wanted in a husband. After this, we attended some of the Hunter meetings in Florida. I had known the Hunters for many years. We became friends and I would take them all around Minneapolis after being healed at one of their meetings.

The Hunters didn't know Dr. Le Roy very well, but when we were in Florida, having just been married for a short time, the Hunters were having some meetings in Ft. Pierce and another place. We went over there, and Dr. Le Roy was following them around. Perhaps even without knowing Dr. Le Roy too well, Charles thought maybe he could trust this guy a little bit. So, he got his first opportunity to minister with Charles Hunter when a fellow came up walking with a limp. Charles said, "Doc, why don't you grow out his legs?" So, Dr. Le Roy had the man sit in a chair (here's his big chance for God to use him) and tried to find that little ankle knob that we're supposed to put our thumbs on (as instructed in the Hunter's "How To Heal The Sick" book). Well, this man had the smoothest leg Dr. Le Roy had ever felt. Dr. Le Roy found out the guy had an artificial limb. God did minister to him through Dr. Le Roy, and in time, he got to know and minister with the Hunters. In August of 1984, Charles and Frances ordained both of in Minneapolis.

Dr. Le Roy retired from his chiropractic business in Green Bay, Wisconsin. He closed his office and sold his equipment. We went forth with the Impossible Miracles Ministry, which is headquartered out of Minneapolis, Minnesota. The Hunters invited us to be on the healing team for their first Healing Explosion in Pittsburgh, Pennsylvania, on July 4, 1985. Along with continuing the Impossible Miracles Ministry on our own, we have attended most of the Healing Explosions in the United States since that first one.

Now we are seeing more signs and wonders in our

ministry than ever before. It is an exciting life, ministering
for the Lord and we are thoroughly enjoying it.

This book is not intended to be a treatise, or formal
medical discussion or reference book, but rather an
informative discussion of some of the ways we have learned
to minister healing by the power of God's Holy Spirit, in
the Name of Jesus. These are guidelines or suggestions
we have seen work to bring about healings, and we believe
if you will try these ways, after having received the
enduement of power by receiving the baptism with the
Holy Spirit, you will be able to see substantial increases
in ministering healing biblically. I try to avoid applying
my chiropractic training and experiences when ministering
healing divinely, but there are many similar exercises which
work, whether by the abilities of a chiropractor, or by the
power of God. We prefer to apply the power of God in
the Name of Jesus, giving the glory to Jesus.

CHAPTER TWO

The Spinal Column

I believe if we are cognizant of the structure and functions of the spinal column (or vertebral column) and its parts, we will have a better understanding of why our body may not be well.

In layman's language, the spinal column is the extension of the brain containing about 100,000 nerves, through which the brain sends all signals, telling every part of your body what to do and when to do it. When a nerve is pinched because the spine is out of alignment, it can cut off the spinal fluid (which insulates the nerve). The result of this is usually quite painful.

When the wires to a microphone are disconnected, it will not work. Neither will a part of the body function properly if its direction giver (the nerve) is disconnected.

The spinal column consists of vertebrae and discs. The discs, which are little cushions between each of the vertebrae, are cartilage-type tissues and can easily be injured. These cushions keep the vertebrae apart and give the spine flexibility. If a vertebra is twisted, the disc will slide out the opposite side and no longer protect one side of that vertebra. This bulge is called a "herniated disc" and it may rupture inside the spinal cord (see illustration below).

Five Lumbar Vertebrae

Herniated Disc

14

The Spine

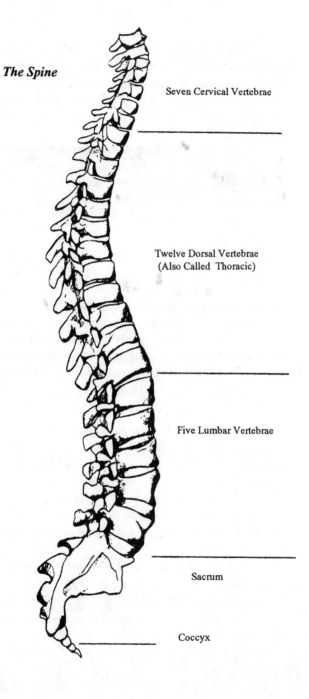

Seven Cervical Vertebrae

Twelve Dorsal Vertebrae
(Also Called Thoracic)

Five Lumbar Vertebrae

Sacrum

Coccyx

These vertebrae encase the two tiny tubes through which the spinal fluid flows to and from the brain. All this is held together by ligaments and muscles, all the way down the spine. You have a series of ligaments which go down the back, and another series of ligaments which go down the front.

Ligaments are not like muscles because they don't stretch, but neither do ligaments get tired like muscles do. Also, ligaments do not have the circulation to them a muscle does; thus, they take longer to heal. When there is damage to a ligament, the muscle is overworked and this may result in a muscle spasm or a kink in your back. Also, this usually results in the formation of scar tissue and adhesions, which are painful in themselves.

Another point of great interest is the fact that no matter what the condition your spinal column, your eyes will always look straight ahead. Scoliosis is a name given for a spinal curvature in the shape of an "S." The effect of this is that your eyes keep looking straight ahead after a part of the spinal column is curved or dislocated. Also, many people have neck curvatures because it compensates to keep the eye direction straight.

So you will understand a little better, we will divide this discussion of the spinal column into three sections: the cervical vertebrae, the dorsal vertebrae, and the lumbar vertebrae.

Looking at the diagram of the spine on page 14, you will notice that it begins at the back of the head (the occiput) and ends at the sacrum (the sacred bone).

The sacrum is the primary respiratory reflex. When you are born and the doctor tips you upside down and taps you on the sacrum, a movement like a pendulum begins as you inhale, then exhale. All your life you continue to inhale, then exhale. Now, I want you to remember this, it is the important part. When you die, you must exhale. I'm serious about this, you know. You can't die unless you

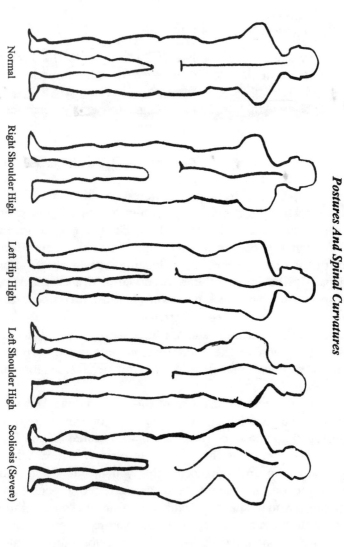

Postures And Spinal Curvatures

Normal

Right Shoulder High

Left Hip High

Left Shoulder High

Scoliosis (Severe)

Posture And Spinal Curvatures

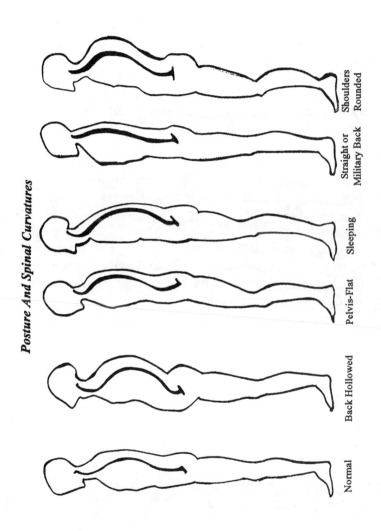

exhale. God gives you your breath at birth and you give
it back at death.

"Sacrum" is a Latin word meaning "sacred." That is
one of the most important parts of the body because this
is the weight-bearing part of your body. All the weight
in your body rests on it.

Every time you breathe, while the sacrum pulls down,
the occiput, up at the top of the spine, pulls in the opposite
direction. That's what pumps the spinal fluid up and down
your spinal column from your brain. So, it is very important
that the spinal column does not get crooked for then it
will block the pumping up and down of this fluid. The
phenomenal thing about it is that the spinal fluid is
pumped up and down at the same time. Can you imagine
anything like that? The life part of your body is in the
spinal fluid.

For instance, if you have a stomach ache, the vertebra
is twisted a little bit, pinching the tube I'm talking about.

Such a restriction of the flow of the spinal fluid may
also result in too much spinal fluid up in your head causing
you to get dizzy.

Your posture is also affected by the position of your
sacrum. When your sacrum is tilted backward, you will have
what is known as "straight back" or "military back" (see
diagrams on pages 16 and 17). When your sacrum is tilted
forward, you will have too much curvature in your spine.

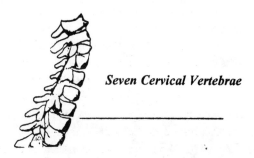

Seven Cervical Vertebrae

The Cervical Vertebrae

Now, we're going to divide up the vertebrae a little bit. At the top of the spinal column you have seven cervical vertebrae. We call them "neck bones" because people can remember that better. The neck bones are very flexible. They bend very easily because the muscles in the neck are the weakest muscles in the body. That is why your head can flop around. Thus, for example, when riding in a car and it gets hit from the back, or stumbling while walking, your head is easily thrown back.

The cervical vertebrae contain the nerves which go to the head, neck and throat. They affect problems such as allergies, chronic tiredness, dizziness, ear problems, eye problems, fainting, hay fever, headaches, high blood pressure, hoarseness, insomnia, migraines, nervous break-downs and nervousness, neuralgia, neuritis, sinus problems, skin disorders, sore throat and stiff neck.

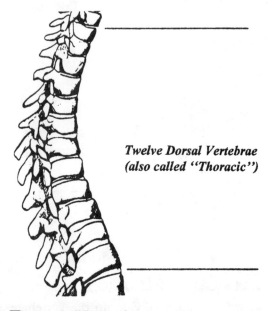

*Twelve Dorsal Vertebrae
(also called "Thoracic")*

The Dorsal Vertebrae

Next, we will discuss the thoracic vertebrae. These are known as the "dorsal vertebrae," twelve in number. We call them dorsals because of the dorsal fin on a fish. People can remember that. These dorsal vertebrae are all attached to ribs and don't bend very much.

The dorsal vertebrae contain nerves which go to the shoulders, chest, upper back, heart, lungs, gall bladder, liver, kidneys, stomach and intestines. They affect such problems as arm pain or numbness, asthma, blood circulation and adrenal problems, bronchial conditions, bursitis, chest pains, congestions, coughs, fever, gall bladder problems, hand pain or numbness, heartburn, heart problems, hives, jaundice, pleurisy, shingles, shoulder pain, stomach problems, throat problems, thyroid conditions, and ulcers.

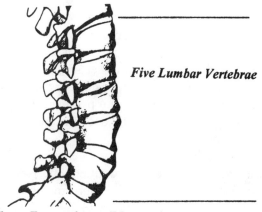

Five Lumbar Vertebrae

The Lumbar Vertebrae

Finally the lower section of the spinal column contains the lumbar vertebrae or the bottom five vertebrae. The lumbars are familiar to most people because this and the neck are the most vulnerable to damage. The very last bone is the sacrum, which we have already mentioned as being the weight-bearing part of the spinal column. Also in this area of the sacrum is the hip bone, which is attached to the leg bone. The sacroiliac is between the pelvic bones. It is a joint composed of the sacrum and bordered on each side by the two iliac bones.

The lumbar vertebrae contain the nerves which go to the appendix, bowels, genitals, bladder and lower limbs. They affect problems such as ankle swelling, backaches, bed wetting, blood circulation problems, cold feet, constipation, diarrhea, dyspepsia, hemorrhoids, hiccoughs, impotence, knee pain, leg cramps, menstrual cramps, prostate problems, rectal itching and problems, rheumatism, sitting pain, sterility and varicose veins.

Your body will appear to have either a short arm or leg when your spine and/or pelvic area is out of alignment. When you are ministering healing to someone whose leg appears to be short, their hip bone may be turned back, and when it goes into place, the legs will be even. Also, when that hip bone goes backwards, it makes your top rib go out of place.

When a person has a short leg, if you will feel right alongside the last cervical vertebra in the neck, you will find a sore spot, and there's also another sore spot on the part of the bone right behind the ear, which is the mastoid part of the temporal bone. When the top rib and temporal bone go backwards, the body will be out of alignment and it affects you all over your body.

For instance, let's say a person is duck footed. That tells you that the pelvic bones are tilted out too wide (unfolded like a book). So when you minister healing to someone, command the pelvic bones to rotate inwardly (like a book being closed). If a person is pigeon toed, that tells you that the pelvic bones are tilted in, that is because the pelvis is out of alignment.

If you never learn another thing, but you learn to grow out the legs, eventually, all of these other misalignments will take care of themselves. For instance, with a short leg, if the hip goes out, the vertebrae in the lower part of the back will follow. If the vertebrae are misaligned severely, this curvature of the spine forms a scoliosis in your body.

Many people are born with injuries which affect the back. In the development of our body, when we're first born, we don't have any ribs, it's all cartilage. That is why it is so important for younger children to refrain from doing work that is too heavy, because they get the rib cage all out of sync since the ribs do not form into bone until you are about twenty years old. They form into bone from the back to the front.

A short leg will affect all of your body from top to bottom. It will affect your temporal bone (back of your ear), it will affect the top rib, the lumbar vertebrae and it may cause a pain in your knee or lower leg.

It is important for women that their pelvic be in alignment, especially during child bearing years. When a baby is born, the pubic bone separates and the baby comes forward in a natural way. Now, if the pelvic bone is turned backward or forward on one side, this area will not open, and the woman will have trouble with childbirth.

Children who have problems with bedwetting may need to have their legs grown out to release the nerves going to the bladder.

The head area should be discussed before we close this chapter. The position of the temporal bone is very important. If the temporal bone is rotated backward, it is going to cause a lot of trouble with your TMJ, which stands for "temporo mandibular joint" (in front of your ears). Through this TMJ passes 35% of all the nerve impulses which go to your brain. The TMJ muscle is the second strongest muscle in the body. It controls the jaw.

This area is so very important because going up the neck into the head is the carotid artery which is where much of your oxygen and blood flow go to the brain. Likewise, the autonomic nerve system goes through here and down the front of your body to the pelvic area.

Even the shape of your head, like the position of your body in the back and also the back of the brain, is important because you must have a good circulation of the spinal fluid, going up and down the spine. The back of the brain is the area that controls your equilibrium and your motion. It is interesting to note that most children who have trouble walking have an injury to the back of the head.

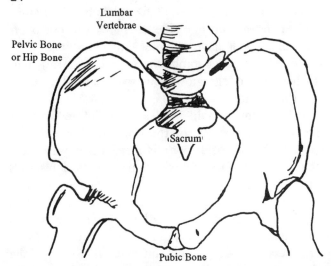

Lumbar
Vertebrae

Pelvic Bone
or Hip Bone

Sacrum

Pubic Bone

It is wonderful to be continually learning. Did you
know that there are various places on the body which are
reflex points, and when these points are touched, they will
indicate problem areas by reflex? As much as I have
studied, I recently learned, for instance, right in the suture
where the occiput joins with the parietal bone, is the spot
where you put your hand to touch the Parkinson reflex.
This is also the spot on your head for the eye reflex.

CHAPTER THREE

Glandular System

The glandular systems greatly affects the way our bodies feel. The various glands will not function properly unless they are receiving the proper signals from the brain through the nerves coming out of the spinal column. Our glands are tissues or organs from which are produced and released useful chemical substances to produce various bodily functions. The glands work together to keep our bodies in good health.

In our head we have the pituitary gland and the pineal gland. In our neck we have the thyroid and the parathyroid. Then there's the thymus gland, which controls our immune system, right in the back of the fifth rib. The adrenal glands are just above your kidneys in the back, right where the last two ribs are. They do not control it entirely, but affect your blood pressure, body temperature and skin as well as other functions.

The sex glands work together with all the glands in the body. That's why when you get a bit older, although your glandular system functions, it doesn't function as it should.

A lot of women notice they begin putting on excess weight when they get about thirty-nine years old. This may be because of the fact that the ovaries, the adrenal and the thyroid glands are not working together the way they should.

Following is a brief review of the various glands to help you understand their importance:

1. Pituitary Gland

This gland is the master gland because it controls and

affects the other glands. Attached to the base of the brain, it produces hormones, which regulate hormone production of the thyroid gland; growth; the development of sexual characteristics; lactation (milky fluid) and hormones which affect our blood pressure, kidney functions and contraction of the uterus.

2. Pineal Gland

Although the functions of this gland are not proven, it is believed to be vitally important to various bodily functions, including sexual development and reproduction.

3. Thyroid Gland

This gland is in the front of the neck and controls the rate of our metabolism. It secretes thyroxin (an iodine compound) into our blood. It controls oxygen in our blood by burning up calories. It also controls the function of the esophagus and the stomach. The thyroid has some effect on the heart muscles causing the heart to beat regularly.

Often, as we get older, our glands don't function in unison. Especially when women age, the thyroid gets sluggish and it doesn't put enough oxygen in the blood to burn up all the excess calories resulting in weight increase.

4. Parathyroid Glands

These glands are found in the front of the neck close to the thyroid gland and consist of four small glands which function as one gland. The secretion from these glands is important to bone growth and the functions of the muscles and nerves by regulating the amount of calcium and phosphate in the body.

5. Thymus Gland

The thymus gland is behind the breastbone in the upper chest. It aids in forming white blood cells for protection against disease. It is a vital part of the body's immune system.

6. Adrenal Glands

The adrenals rest on the upper part of each kidney at the bottom part of the ribs. One of their functions is to keep us in tune with our surroundings. The adrenal glands affect the pores of our skin, and when we get too warm, the little muscles which control the pores of the skin relax and we perspire. The little muscles controlling the sweat glands will contract when we are chilled and our skin gets those little bumps. They also secrete hormones which influence various bodily functions such as carbohydrate metabolism, kidney action, retention of sodium in the body and sexual characteristics.

These glands produce adrenalin which contracts capillaries and stimulates the sympathetic nervous system.

The adrenal glands are affected by our emotions. They raise our sugar level and make our immune system go awry, and this allows germs to grow.

Do you know that bitterness and resentment start with anger? If we get upset, angry or stressful, these glands will produce an overabundance of adrenalin to our body. Our body cannot absorb the excessive amount of adrenalin that shoots out and as a result, it goes into the kidneys, which are unable to carry off this excess. Where does it go then? It settles in the joints of the body which causes arthritis. Of course, this is not the only cause of arthritis, but according to statistics, it is one of the most significant.

7. Sex Glands

The sex glands are located in the lower back. They relate to our sexual development and reproduction.

CHAPTER FOUR

The Immune System

Fifty years ago, when I went to school, they didn't talk much about the body's immune system. They would talk about catching a cold, though. The immune system is the body's ability to overcome disease or infection. Recent studies have shown that the immune system may fail to recognize a problem, such as cancer cells. Thus, it is important that we take authority over our immune system in the Name of Jesus.

To minister to the immune system, start by commanding the immune system to recognize any foreign cells, such as cancer cells, and to send out antibodies to locate and destroy these foreign cells. Also, command the immune system's memory to continue doing this. Also, speak to your blood system and command that it produce healthy blood cells and that it not allow cancer cells to grow.

Others areas important to healing and health respond to us taking authority over the organs and their functions. The results of our authoritative healing command is that the power of God's Holy Spirit is dispensed or released in the Name of Jesus. Some of the important parts to which we should thus speak are:

Command the pelvis to go into place.
Command the lumbar vertebrae and muscles and ligaments to be healed and to return to their natural position and strength. This will loosen the nerves which go to the bladder.
Then command the bladder to be healed and command the kidneys to be healed because the bladder, the kidneys, the lungs and the

30

bronchials all work together with your sinuses and your skin. Your kidneys clear out the infection in your body. Infection has to go through your kidneys. If your bladder isn't working properly, the kidneys can't work properly. If the kidneys don't work then, of course, all that toxin and poison circulating through your body comes through your liver. When the liver gets loaded up, the toxin then tries to go out through the lungs, sinuses or skin.

CHAPTER FIVE

The Muscular System

A brief overview of the body's muscular system will help us understand why it is important that our muscles be relaxed, toned, strengthened and in proper position.

The body contains over 600 major muscles, all of which relate to various bodily functions.

There are three types of muscle: (1) skeletal, (2) smooth and (3) cardiac.

The cardiac muscle, which makes up the walls of the heart, is stimulated by the autonomic nervous system. When the cardiac muscle contracts, it pushes the blood out of the heart, into the arteries and throughout the body.

The smooth muscles (involuntary muscles) are found in various body organs, such as the walls of the stomach, the bladder and blood vessels. They operate automatically and slowly in a rhythmic pattern of contraction which is followed by relaxation. This automatic function causes our organs to process food, blood, etc. An example would be the food we eat is moved through the stomach and intestines for digestion by these smooth muscles.

Muscles of which we are more aware are the skeletal muscles (sometimes called "voluntary" muscles). They are the ones most frequently injured. These skeletal muscles make our body move. They hold the various organs, bones and body parts in place, and they also give shape to our body.

Most of these skeletal muscles connect to our bones by tendons, which are tough, yet flexible connecting tissues. They usually operate in pairs, one will cause the bones to extend out while the other will cause them to bend. Movement of these muscles is stimulated by nerve impulses.

When the normal operation of a muscle is disturbed, these muscles may cramp or even go into spasms, both of which can be extremely painful. Diseases causing muscle deterioration are usually related to nervous system malfunctions which cut off stimulation to the muscles.

We have mentioned tendons in this section and their function, and we also want to briefly mention ligaments. Ligaments are tissues which hold the body's organs in place and they also fasten bones together. They are as strong as rope and are grouped together in cords or bands or sheets and cover joints. A sprain, for example, is a partial tearing or twisting of a ligament covering a joint.

It is important to realize that when our spinal column is out of sync, this may well affect the signals the nerves coming out from the spinal column send to the muscles. This, in turn, will affect the function of the part of the body the particular muscles affect.

CHAPTER SIX

Spiritual Applications To Healing

Spirit, Soul and Body

In addition to physical applications, there are many spiritual applications to healing. Even though there is a lot about healing we don't understand, knowledge about healing is rapidly increasing. In III John 2, the Bible tells us, "Beloved, I wish above all things that thou mayest prosper and be in health, even as thy soul prospereth." Now, we may wonder, how does our soul prosper?

This chapter will give us a clearer understanding of how our soul prospers. Our bodies and minds are prospering when we are in good health.

There are compound names of God, one of which is Jehovah Rapha, meaning "the God who heals." He not only heals our body, He also heals our spirit and our soul.

Spirit

When we are born again, we actually receive a portion of the mind of Christ. If you hear someone talk about an out-of-the-body experience where the spirit leaves their body, they generally were up above their body. They can look down and see their body, yet the spirit looks exactly like their body, except you can see through it like looking through a thin cloud The spirit is an exact outline of our body.

Now, if we look at our brain and our nervous system,

we also find that if we stood our brain and nervous system by themselves, they would be a perfect outline of our body.

When we receive the baptism with the Holy Spirit, we receive power. Our spirits, the size of our bodies, are filled with God's Holy Spirit, which endues us with the miracle-producing power which when dispensed into sick bodies or minds in the Name of Jesus, heals them. That's the power with which Jesus healed the sick.

We should learn how to use that power in healing other people. We know that all healing takes place in the Name of Jesus. I've been practicing chiropractic laying on of hands on people for over forty years, and I know that after I received the baptism with the Holy Spirit, patients could feel something that they never felt before. I didn't at first know what it was, but now I know that it is the power of the Holy Spirit!

There is a difference in your life. Many times you can work all day long and never get tired. When your spirit and mind have been renewed, your reasoning is renewed, and your thinking will be on the things of the Lord.

As you are working your way through life, as a professional or whatever, you will find your thinking is proper, your mind is renewed and your memory is healthy. Your reasoning is more accurate because the Holy Spirit gives you ideas on how to conduct your business or ideas on how to do your work at home if you are a housewife or a homemaker.

He gives you ideas on how to raise your family, what to say and what not to say. The Holy Spirit works in us, and our lives reflect the fruit of the Spirit. Love, joy, peace, long-suffering, temperance, faithfulness, kindness, meekness and goodness can be produced in our lives. We will be able to reason. We will be able to know what to do because, if we listen, the Holy Spirit will tell us what to do. Our attitudes reflect the nature of God when we follow after the Holy Spirit.

Soul

The soul is actually the eternal part of us that does all the thinking, reasoning, etc. Our soul will tell our mind what to remember, how to reason and what to think. Our mind is the part of our body that responds to what the soul tells it to do. Our emotions come from our soul.

As we read the Word of God, our mind is renewed, our emotions are healed and we join our will with the will of the Father. As we live in His will, then we will prosper. Our soul will prosper as our mind is being renewed. We become one with the Lord our God. We have to be careful what we read, what we hear, what we taste, what we smell and what we feel. They all influence our life.

Satan uses our senses to get at us. He tries to influence and control our mind. My wife, Norma Jean, and I have found in our "Impossible Miracles Ministry" that a lot of people have emotional problems. Many times they have unforgiveness in their lives.

The reason God wants to forgive our sins is so that He can forget them. When our sins are forgiven, they are forgotten by God and we should consider in our minds and hearts that they don't exist. That is the way we should dismiss unforgiveness. If God forgets, we should, too! God throws them into the sea of forgetfulness, never to be remembered again.

We have provided a special section on unforgiveness in this book as shared by Norma Jean because unforgiveness results in many complications in one's life.

Body

Our body is that earthly vessel which contains our spirit and soul. Our body will respond to our soul. If our soul is led by the Holy Spirit, then our body will conform to the Word of God. If our soul is not led by the Holy Spirit, but follows its own desires, our body will reflect symptoms of improper care. If stress is prevalent in our life, our body will often react with stomach problems or nervousness. On the other hand, if we trust God, maintaining the peace of God during stressful circumstances, and do not react to stress, our body will get proper food and rest and be in good health.

Often we think of our mind and our brain as being the same. Actually, our mind expresses itself over our brain. Our brain is the beginning of the nervous system. As we talk or think, we are telling our body what to do. An example of this is when we are very tired, our mind tells our nerves to contract muscles and our neck will get tight.

CHAPTER SEVEN

Ministering Healing

It is important for us to always have a positive attitude in life, and to notice how much better we are rather than how bad we feel. Jesus is always positive and Satan is always negative. Our physical condition will be influenced by our attitude, good or bad. If you let Satan limit what you *expect* to receive, he will limit what you *will* receive.

Remember all healing is done BY THE POWER OF THE HOLY SPIRIT IN THE NAME OF JESUS.

Now let's begin ministering healing.

Because the major source of physical problems stems from the spine, we feel it is important in most healings to minister first to the spine, and then to other diseases or injuries as we become aware of them.

We do not feel anyone ministering healing with the power of God's Holy Spirit, in the Name of Jesus, should ever make a diagnosis of the problems of anyone to whom you are ministering healing. Let the person with the need of healing tell you what their problem is. Even doctors who know the human body and many remedies of illnesses or injuries are very interested in knowing what the patient feels is wrong. Ask lots of questions to develop from the person what is actually wrong with their body. Also, we urge you never to remove a medical aid such as a neck collar or brace, a back brace, an ace bandage or any such thing because when a doctor tells them to wear these, he should be the one to tell them to stop wearing them. The same is true of medication; we should never tell someone to stop their medication - let the doctor who prescribed it tell them when to stop taking the medication.

Ministering Healing To
The Lower Spine

When we are ministering to the spine or bone structure of the body, we generally prefer to start with what we call the leg thing, or growing out legs. This is simply a way of laying on hands and commanding healings or adjustments, all by the power of God's Holy Spirit and in the Name of Jesus.

Growing out legs is always exciting because the person being ministered to can watch their legs appear to grow out when you release the power of God into the back.

In order to measure the legs, which is an outward

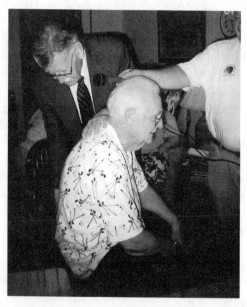

evidence of a lower back (lumbar area) being out of adjustment or muscles, ligaments and tendons being stretched or jammed or pulled or damaged in some way. The following procedure should be followed:

Have the person sit on a straight chair (it can be done

on the ground or floor if a chair is not available), with their hips tight against the back of the chair so they will be sitting straight (not slumped). Ask them to look straight forward. Ask them to stretch their legs forward, or you pick up the legs; hold the legs straight, not crooked. Then put the ends of your thumbs on each of the ankle bones, holding your thumbs straight so they are perpendicular to the ground and so the knuckles and thumbnails are facing one another. This allows for an accurate measurement of the length of the legs.

Tell the person to watch your thumbs, one of which will show a short leg, and tell them that when you release the power of the Holy Spirit in Jesus' Name, the short leg will appear to grow out. Speak to the back to be healed (whatever you determine is wrong with it). For instance, if they have a herniated disc, say something like, "I command a new disc to be created and in the right position, the muscles, ligaments, tendons and nerves to be healed, go into the right position and length, in Jesus' Name." Then say, "Watch your leg grow!"

Watching the power of God actually moving the back into the place by watching the leg appear to grow will build their faith, and almost always they will be healed. Have them immediately stand up, bend over, and say, "Thank You, Jesus," and then tell them to put their faith into action by bending their back forward, backward, side to side, and then ask, "WHAT HAPPENED TO THE PAIN?" (assuming they had pain). Watch their face as they excitedly discover they have been healed!

Healings which are done by growing out legs include such other things as

Intestines
Appendix
Bowels
Colon
Genitals
Bladder

If they tell you they have a problem with these or other parts in the lower part of the body, command in Jesus' Name these parts to be healed. If necessary, command creative miracles. See Romans 4:17 which says in part, "and calleth those things which be not as though they were."

Should their problem be the tailbone (coccyx), command it to be healed and move into its proper position. It is amazing to watch God bend that little bone back into place and stop all pain.

If you feel from what the person has told you that you might want to add something, then add something like this (depending upon their problem), "I command the circulation going to these parts of the body to be healed and the blood vessels cleared of any foreign material buildup, and for the swelling (if applicable) to be healed."

Often, when one leg appears shorter than the other, you will discover that likely their hipbone, collarbone and temporal bone will be turned backwards on the same side as the short leg, perhaps causing the eustachian tube to be under pressure. This is the cause of many hearing problems. Many times as the leg grows out, adjusting the lumbar spine, your body will adjust all the way to your head, and can result in the temporal bone returning to its proper position.

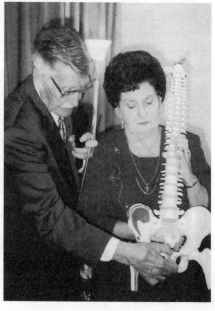

Ministering Healing To The Pelvic Area

The sacroiliac is located between the pelvic bones. In my estimation, the sacroiliac is the most important physical part of the body. It is the shock absorber of the body. The sacroiliac joint is composed of the sacrum, the weight-bearing part of the body, bordered on each side by the ilium bones, the flat bones you feel when you place your hands on your hips. At the end of the sacrum is the tailbone.

At the top or the base of the sacrum, the lumbar vertebrae rest. As mentioned earlier, every time you breathe, the sacrum rocks back and forth and pulls the covering of the spinal cord. This pumps the spinal fluid up and down the cord from your brain. The sacroiliac joint is the only joint in your body that doesn't have muscles holding it. It only has ligaments. It doesn't move very much, but it does move.

We will go now to the pelvic area and do "The Pelvic Thing." Stand upright with your hands or fingers on your pelvic or hip bones and your feet a couple of inches apart.

In the Name of Jesus command the ligaments of your pelvic joint to be relaxed. Command the muscles to be relaxed in your pelvic area and command your pelvis to be adjusted. Command the sacrum to be adjusted. (They may start to sway a little bit at this point because of the power of God.) I like to encourage the person to twist and turn then a little bit and command the pelvis to be adjusted.

As this takes place, tell them to say, "Thank You, Jesus." If the pelvis moves from side to side, this means the person has a short leg. If it moves from front to back, they will usually have a lumbar problem and most likely adhesions and scar tissue.

Now command all the muscles and ligaments of the lower lumbar area (the lower part of the back--the last five vertebrae) to relax and be in proper position and of proper strength. This may have already been accomplished with the "leg thing." Command all scar tissues and adhesions to be healed. Command the lumbar vertebrae to be adjusted in the Name of Jesus.

Now, tell the person to bend back and forth and sway a little bit sideways.

As they do this, that is the time when the adjustment takes place and the vertebrae go into their proper positions.

Females should command the ligaments around the ovaries to be relaxed and not pinch the ovaries. When a lady has "monthly pains," this is a wonderful way to lessen or stop the pain. It can be done several times a day by the woman herself. Remember to say, "Thank You, Jesus."

Next command the nerves in the lumbar area (they go all the way down your legs) to be free of any pressure.

Command all the muscles in the legs to be relaxed, the ligaments to be relaxed and the pelvic or hip bones to go into place. Have them turn around and bend over again a little bit. You might need to command all the muscles around the knees to be relaxed and the bones to be adjusted. If so, tell the person to bend their knees a little bit. If they have an ankle or foot problem, part of the problem may be corrected when you command the ankle and foot bones to go into place. Then, have the person stand on tiptoe a little bit, slightly moving back and forth, and up and down. You may need to command in the Name of Jesus the ligaments and muscles of the legs to be relaxed or command all the blood vessels in the legs to be healthy and the circulation in their legs to be normal.

Now, this would be a good time to minister again to the lower back. The curvature in the back at the waist should be about one-and-a-quarter inches. If the curvature is not enough or is too much, repeat the pelvic thing, commanding the sacrum to move to the right curvature. This often will heal flat feet.

43

If they have a bladder or kidney problem, command the bladder and the kidneys to be healed so the kidneys can eliminate any toxin and poison in the blood.

Now, with your hands on their hips, command the lymphatic system to function normally (the lymphatic system is the one that takes care of the extra fluid in the body) and to take care of all the excess fluid in their body. They may have a problem with the white or red blood cells. If so, command the lymphatic system to manufacture white cells and other types of cells that fight infection in the body.

Remember, have them say, "Thank You, Jesus."

Command the bone marrow in their bones to manufacture good red blood cells. That's what puts a glow in the cheeks and a spring in the step.

Ministering Healing To The Shoulders, Arms and Upper Back

To measure the length of arms (which varies when there is a problem in the upper spine--the dorsal area-- or the ribs) have the person stand up straight with their feet even and looking straight ahead. Have them drop their hands to their sides, relax and swing the hands back and forth a little. Tell them to relax their arms and stretch them straight ahead from their shoulders. Say, "Stretch them out!"

Ask the person to put their hands together, palm facing palm, but not quite touching. Have them bend their elbows and look at the tips of the fingers to see if they are even. If they are not even, that might mean one side of their shoulders is a little bit higher than the other side. Have them stretch their arms and hands forward again and command the muscles and ligaments in the shoulders and chest to be relaxed in the Name of Jesus.

Command the dorsal vertebrae to be adjusted, and then have them say, "Thank You, Jesus."

Command the nerves going down to their fingers, elbows and shoulders to be relaxed. Command the circulation in their arms and hands to be normal. Have them wiggle their shoulders a little, turn their elbows, wrists and fingers.

You might need to minister to other problems relating to growing out arms.

If some of the following exist, command all the joints to be healed in the Name of Jesus.

Command the balls and sockets of the joints to be smooth and to function properly.

Command the ribs to be adjusted. Have them move the shoulders around a little bit, up and down and back. As you do this, sometimes they will feel a little popping. This often happens when the bones are going into place. As they move their shoulders, ask them to take a deep breath or two. They may feel the shoulder joints becoming a bit more movable.

Other healings may be accomplished, such as:

Command the dorsal vertebrae to be free of pressure. These are the nerves which go to the esophagus and down to the opening of the stomach.

Command the opening of the stomach to be relaxed so the gall bladder, pancreas and liver can drain.

Command any inflammation of the stomach to be gone.

Command the glands in the stomach to manufacture enzymes for digestion.

Command the nerves going to heart to be relaxed so the heart can beat in steady rhythm, and command that the muscles of the heart be strong in the Name of Jesus.

Command the nerves going to the lungs and the bronchial tubes to be relaxed so breathing can be normal. Have the person take a couple of deep breaths.

Command the lungs to be free of any mucous or infection, in the Name of Jesus.

Command the nerves going to the diaphragm to be relaxed and the diaphragm to be strong and in place. Have the person take another couple of deep breaths. As they exercise their diaphragm, have them say, "Thank You, Jesus."

Office workers do a great deal of turning around while sitting. This may cause the vertebrae between the shoulders and rib cage to get out of alignment. Command all the vertebrae between the shoulders to be adjusted and then command the ribs to be adjusted. Also, command all the muscles and ligaments in the back to be relaxed and the ribs to go into place.

Isn't it amazing that the power of the Holy Spirit can accomplish so many different healings as they are needed! Jesus not only gave us this power and authority, but gave us the responsibility of healing the sick!

Ministering Healing To The Head And Neck

To minister to the head and neck area, we do what Charles and Frances Hunter have termed "The Neck Thing." When ministering to another, place your thumbs in front of the ears and wrap your fingers around the side and back of the person's neck. Hold the head firmly--but not too tightly--relaxing your hands. Have the person move their head gently up and down, from side to side and in a circular motion, commanding the cervical vertebrae and discs to be healed and adjusted in the Name of Jesus. Command any scar tissue or adhesions in the neck to be healed in the Name of Jesus.

As they are bowing their head down, command the Atlas (that's the top vertebra) to adjust. It is easy to remember this as the "yes" bone. Then, have the person move their head from side to side command the Axis (that's the second vertebra) to be healed and adjusted. This is easy to remember as the "no" bone. What you are actually doing is stimulating all the nervous energy that goes through the TMJ up to the brain.

Next, slip your hands down a little bit, just above the shoulders in that area of the neck and command those lower cervical vertebrae and discs and the upper dorsal vertebrae and discs to be adjusted in the Name of Jesus.

To minister to yourself, place your little finger and the one next to it in front of your ears and your thumb and remaining fingers around the side and back of your neck. Turn your head from side to side, forward and back, then tilt your head to the side until it almost touches your shoulder. Tilt it the other way until it almost touches your other shoulder. Command all those nerves going down to your shoulders, elbows and hands to be normal. Wiggle your shoulders around a little bit, turn around, up and down slightly, turn your elbows, exercise your elbows, exercise your wrists and your fingers, and command all the joints to be healed in Jesus' Name.

Now, go back to the upper part of your neck, put your hands just below your ears again, the fingers at the back of the neck. Command those upper cervical vertebrae to be adjusted so the nerves are free. Those are the nerves which go through your TMJ joint, just below your ears.

Command those nerves to be free so that the circulation up to the brain is normal. That is the TMJ joint being healed. Command the autonomic nervous system to function properly. Command the muscles and ligaments in the TMJ to be normal. Open and close your mouth a couple of times, exercise that TMJ and say, "Thank You, Jesus."

Now, if you have an ear problem, with your hands on your ears, around your ears and in the back of your neck, command the nerves going to your ears to be free of pressure, command the circulation to your ears to be normal. Command the auditory nerve and all the hair-like nerves in your ears to be healed and function properly. Also, command the blood vessels to be loosed and to function properly. Command all those little bones in your ears to be adjusted in the Name of Jesus, as they cause us to hear clearly. Command the eustachian tube to be free from pressure. Now, command the spirit of deafness to come out in the Name of Jesus...and say, "Thank You, Jesus!"

To minister healing to your eyes (or someone else's), place your fingers of one hand in front of your eyes and the other hand on the back of your head, command the optic nerve to be healed and adjusted. Command the circulation in your eyes to be normal, and the blood vessels to be normal. Command the muscles of your eyes to be relaxed so that the eyeball has the perfect form that it needs. Command the pressure in the eyes to be normal and the fluid in your eyes to be normal in the Name of Jesus. Now, command a creative miracle in your eyes, restoring them to 20/20 vision in the Name of Jesus, and say, "Thank You, Lord! Glory to God!"

Your skull is made up of many bones, so if you need a healing there, place your hands on top of your head and command all those cranial bones to be adjusted in the Name of Jesus.

Other parts may be ministered to if they have a need such as:

Facial bones: put your hands on your face and command the facial bones to be adjusted. While slowly turning your head from side to side and backward and forward, command all the muscles and ligaments to relax. Command all scar tissue and any adhesions to be healed.

Place one hand on your forehead and one on the back of your head and command the pituitary gland to be normal and to function properly.

Command all other glands to function properly, skin to be healthy and body to be free from allergies and allergic reactions.

Place your hand on the neck and command the thyroid and para-thyroid to function properly and in unison with the other glands.

There is an area in the back of your head, slightly above the occiput, where the mastoid is located. That's the area that regulates your sleep (we call it the "sleepastat".) Gently rub this area as you command the mastoid to be relaxed to help you sleep better.

Almost everyone is interested in controlling their appetite. To minister to your appetite, place your hand on the back of your head in the indention at the base of your skull where the skull connects above the first vertebra. This is the area which regulates your appetite (we call it the "appestat") Command the appestat to be adjusted to its upper limit. This will signal when you have the proper amount to eat. Dr. Mary Ruth Swope, a dietician and nutritionist who has attended many of the Hunter Healing Explosions, ministers in this area. She prayed for the appestat to be adjusted to its upper limit because once you have eaten and taken a break from your meal for any reason, by the time you come back to your plate, you discover that you are not as hungry as you were before. This is because once you have eaten some food, your blood sugar level came up. When you pray for someone's appestat, the blood sugar level comes up faster. The more you eat, the slower your blood sugar comes up. People get so used to eating a lot of food that the appestat doesn't work properly.

Do this routinely, nearly every day. The main thing is to be consistent because it's your health that you are promoting and this procedure gives you practice, enabling you to minister to other people, too. Now, if you do this every day, you'll develop a little routine to follow, and you might want to make some changes yourself as you go through it because practice makes perfect. Remember, we get the blessings and God gets the glory.

Ministering In Unexpected Circumstances

Like my initial opportunity to minister with Charles Hunter when he asked me grow out the leg of the man with an artificial limb, you will meet unexpected circumstances, but "nothing is impossible for God." We can adjust to any circumstance. In the case of the man with the artificial limb, we were still able to minister God's power to adjust his pelvic area and alleviate his pain. Perhaps you will minister to a person who has had a limb either partially or fully amputated. In that case, you just place your hands on the nearest joint location and command the adjustments from that point. When ministering to a person in a wheelchair who is unable to raise their legs, find a spot such as the knees, which had the same protrusion. You can place your hands on shoulders and command the arms to be even if someone cannot straighten their arms.

I would like to mention also that if you are ministering to a stroke victim, put your hand on top of the head, just above the ear on the opposite side of the stroke. Bind Satan, cast out the spirit of death because some brain cells have died as a result of the stroke, in Jesus' Name and command a creative miracle (a new brain and nervous system). It is helpful to work with the person's arm, leg, wrist, and ankle. Help the person with the stroke exercise each of these joints, gently and carefully at first; then have the person do all he or she can to begin using their own strength and own brain signals to being moving the part(s) with which you are working.

Start with the paralyzed or partially paralyzed arm, bending the arm at the elbow several times with your own effort, never forcing the movement, but gradually increasing the amount you bend as it loosens. Then do the wrist and fingers. Then lift the arm upward, not forcing but applying a gentle movement to help the person. Have the person do all he or she can to lift it, but guide it as it is lifted, and finally, if possible, have them lift it all the way straight up.

Then apply the same exercise to the leg and ankle, extending the leg with each movement until it finally straightens all the way out if possible. Do the same with the ankle as though he or she is patting their foot.

Encourage the person as you work with each of these parts. If they say it hurts, command the spirit of pain to leave, and then say, "Now it won't hurt!" There will generally be no more pain. They have been expecting it to hurt, but with a little encouragement it will stop hurting.

Tell the person who takes care of them to repeat these exercises daily. This helps restore the ability of the brain to send signals to the limbs. Tell them that they are now exercising the brain, retraining it to tell the body parts to work again. These are probably the same exercises and therapy they have been used to, but tell them that now the brain can transmit signals to these parts. It is very important that they do all the movements by themselves so you can quit helping them.

If they cannot speak or if they have a speech defect, have them repeat simple words, and with continued exercise, to speak phrases or sentences.

CHAPTER EIGHT

Ministering To Children

Many children suffer from bedwetting. This is due to the nerves going to the bladder not functioning properly. Growing out the child's legs will alleviate this problem in most cases.

Children with an equilibrium, motion or walking problem possibly have had an injury to the back of the head.

You will often find that children having colds generally have a short leg because it bothers their bladder. When the bladder malfunctions, the kidneys can't expel the poison from the bloodstream because it has to go through the bladder. If the bladder does not function, the kidneys will take the fluid out of the blood but won't take the poison out. The poison keeps circulating and soon it comes through your sinus or bronchials or some other place, or you might even have skin problems such as psoriasis.

When ministering to babies or very small children, instead of doing the pelvic thing or leg thing as you would do with an adult, just lovingly place your hands on the pelvic bones while the mother hold the child facing you. The leg thing can be done fairly effectively by simply holding the child's little legs out as the mother holds the child facing you. Then make the usual commands in the Name of Jesus.

For a little larger child, you can sit them straight up in a chair and grow out their legs, or do the pelvic thing, as you do an adult, commanding the pelvis to adjust and commanding the lumbar vertebrae to go into proper place.

Another severe problem in small children is high fever. We suggest you rebuke the fever like Jesus did, and command the cause of the fever to be healed.

For homecare by a parent, the following may be applied. First, contact your doctor in the event of high fever or persistent fever. There are many causes of fever, so care must be taken.

52

However, a parent may do the following which can help in many circumstances: hold the child up to your body, placing your arms around the child with your fingers on the spinal column. Find the little ridge and very gently massage or pull the skin to the side of the spinal column. Do one side and then the other, up and down the spinal column. Then wash the child with tepid water, one area at a time and dry the area before washing the next one. This will wipe the toxins away from the child's body as they are coming out through the skin. I feel that this may be repeated every forty-eight minutes. As your hands and body touch the child, you are releasing God's healing power in the Name of Jesus.

The following excerpt is from the book "Handbook For Healing" by Charles and Frances Hunter and is quoted with their permission:

When ministering to children, remember that you are much bigger than they are, and if you are not careful, you may frighten them and lose their confidence.

This principle also applies to adults, especially to those who have never been exposed to divine healing or deliverance. Be careful to approach them in gentleness and love. You may be "full grown" in the supernatural, but they may be as little children and you may frighten them and lose their confidence.

One of the best ways to approach a child is to come down to their level by kneeling. It helps a great deal to always smile and talk to them quietly and confidently. One good way to gain contact with a youngster is to extend your hands to them, palms upward and open, so they can place their hands in yours.

While ministering to them, do not raise your voice. It is possible to continue smiling at the youngster at the same time you are taking authority over an evil spirit and casting it out in Jesus' Name. Speak with authority and that spirit will recognize that you mean business, and it will obey. A child will always recognize when someone is ministering in love, and they will respond. Therefore project to them from the inside of you that you love them and you are there to help them.

CHAPTER NINE

Gradual Healing

As we are ministering healing such as growing out legs and commanding the pelvis to be adjusted, we are not pushing God around or telling God what to do. We are talking to the affliction in the person's body. In the Name of Jesus we can command them to be relaxed. We can command that they breathe normally. We can command their heart to beat normally. We can command many things. We realize that God doesn't heal people to make some evangelist a big time healer. He doesn't heal people because they deserve it. He heals people because they need it. When we see that need and minister the resurrection power of the Holy Spirit to someone, that brings healing from God.

Sometimes, healing takes a little while. For instance, when a person's problem is on the same side on which they have a long leg, this indicates that their problem may be more severe and the healing may take longer. Sometimes the person becomes instantly healed. We always think that while a person is being healed over a period of time, the healing is more pronounced and the healing stays better because sometimes if you're instantaneously healed, a lot of people will think that it just happened that way. They don't realize they have to give credit to the Father, who gives us all good things. In the Name of Jesus we are healed, and we have to realize that.

If a person is 25% better after you have ministered to them, have them say, "Thank You, Jesus." Every time they say, "Thank You, Jesus," their faith grows stronger for their healing.

Sometimes, we have people who have a tremendous amount of healing, but they still have some little pain. Many times these little pains are just symptoms of what's going on. They think it should all be gone. If they would just say,

"Thank You, Jesus," for their healing, the healing can continue. If they don't say anything and give credit where the credit is due, at times, they'll lose their healing.

We have instances where people tell us that after we prayed with them or ministered to them, the next day they felt a lot better. Sometimes, the next day they felt a lot worse. You can get different reactions. We know that everybody doesn't react the same way. Everyone has a different background. We have different ethnic backgrounds, and nationalities even have different types of people.

We minister to some people who don't have sensitive nervous systems, but to some people who have very sensitive nervous systems. It seems that a person with a very sensitive nervous system probably has a few more aches and pains than another person, but at the same time, that person with the sensitive nervous system may learn how to take care of themselves. They learn how to get enough rest and eat a more sensible diet than the person who is never sick. This person rarely takes proper care of themselves, and probably doesn't get enough rest, overworks, and is always on the go. When they do get sick, they don't know what to do because they have never been sick before and they think this is the end, that they are going to die.

I've seen that happen many times. Especially in people who are over fifty years old, who have never been sick in their life and all of a sudden they are not feeling good, they have to have their gall bladder out or some other thing like that. They have to have something done because they think they are going to die since they don't feel well.

CHAPTER TEN

Blockages To Healing

As noted in the foreword, the purpose of this book is to help you minister to yourself, as well as others. You can minister by helping others through an experience you have already had and by sharing knowledge you have obtained.

Norma Jean has a terrific testimony because she has experienced rejection in her life, and if she talks to somebody else who has been rejected, she can minister to that person.

Norma Jean and I both lost our mates, so we can minister to those who have also lost their mate because we know exactly how they feel. As you become familiar with ministering to yourself, you will easily move into ministering to others.

There are many causes of problems and sicknesses and there are things that will block the receiving of a healing. In this chapter we will discuss some of them.

Accidents/Injuries

Trauma or injuries can make people sick. Falls, accidents, and sprains can injure a person. Some people suffer from injuries received at birth, such as pulled ligaments or damaged tendons. We can easily suffer sprains in our elbows, wrists and ankles. There are many injuries which cause the pelvis to be out of place. There are injuries which cause the discs and vertebrae in the neck or back to be out of place.

Allergies

Often allergies are inherited; however, overindulgence may also bring on allergies. Certain geographical areas are predominantly known for having a high percentage of the population suffer with allergies.

Anger

Sometimes people say that they can't help if they have a short temper. Anger, however, is very harmful to your normal bodily functions. Anger increases the adrenalin flow in your

56

body which results in the various organs being overworked.

Anxiety/Stress/Worry

We live in a society where pressure is high to meet deadlines and to be an achiever. Mental worry is prevalent and stress is a major problem for people. Anxiety, stress and worry will cause a hardship on a person's heart and ultimately can disable the person. Many people suffer from irregular heartbeat because of the stress and strain of life. This results also in improper sleep or even stomach ulcers, which are very common to people in stressful jobs or those who live stressful lives.

Jesus spoke to the storm and said, "Peace, be still." We also can overcome these attacks on our minds and bodies by practicing, "Peace, be still."

Attitudes

A lot of people have the wrong attitude about their job. They think that their job is not very significant and they could have a better one. We have to learn to be content.

Paul said in Philippians 4:12,13: "I know both how to be abased, and I know how to abound: every where and in all things I am instructed both to be full and to be hungry, both to abound and to suffer need. I can do all things through Christ which strengtheneth me."

As you work, do your work as unto the Lord and you will be rewarded. Forget about what the boss, or whomever it might be, does that upsets you. It is the same thing with tithing, and with giving. Give as unto the Lord. He is the One who does the rewarding. Remember, people have different kinds of temperaments, but we have God and Christ Jesus in us to help us overcome these negative attacks.

Discontentment

A thing that I think is very important in our lives is to keep ourselves well, happy and contented. We are not to be concerned about what other people are doing. If your neighbor has a new car, it doesn't mean that you have to get one. If your car is running good, just leave it alone. Keep it running. The Bible says in Philippians 4:19, "But my God shall supply all your need according to his riches in glory by Christ Jesus." It doesn't say anything about your wants. That's where a lot of people get into trouble. They have too many wants in life. They think they need this and they think they need that, but they really don't. The Lord is taking care of the needs, but not always their wants.

Discontentment leads to problems because people too often buy something they can't afford, and then they have interest to pay. That makes them anxious and nervous and results in indigestion and quite often brings on fears in their life. One thing leads to another.

We should learn to live a contented life and have the fruit of the Spirit working in our lives to keep us happy and contented just the way we are. Remember, God's Word tells us in Proverbs 17:22, "A merry heart doeth good like a medicine." Without Christ in your life, there seems to be a longing in your soul. This is because there is a spot in your being that only Christ Himself can fill. There is also a longing in your innate being for your body to be healthy and happy. It is miraculous what six to eight glasses of water per day can do for your health.

Envy/Jealousy/Unforgiveness

Envy, jealousy and unforgiveness bring problem after problem into our lives. For instance, unforgiveness overstimulates the adrenal glands in the adrenalin cortical area and affects the manufacture of cortisone in your body. This excessive adrenalin in your body is too much for your organs to process and may result in your suffering from arthritis.

We, at times, have a lot of aches and pains, which may just be symptoms, and many times we do not know what is wrong. If we can get relaxed, we will be surprised at how a lot of these little aches and pains will go away. When they do not go away, they tell us there is something wrong in our

58

body, and we should try to find out what that wrong is.

Relax a little bit, exercise a little bit and have a sensible diet. Get really serious and say, "Oh, Lord, change me into Your likeness." Everything in your life can be changed. When we seek God's laws of health in the Bible and obey what He says, we can overcome many afflictions.

Fears/Superstitions

Excessive fear can lead to much suffering. Fear will cause a person to do things that will bring them harm and, in extreme cases, can disable themselves. Superstitions are often fear related and will cause people to trust in a variety of things rather than in God.

Inherited Problems/Generational Curses

I find that in ministering to people, there are many inherited problems such as ancestors who had problems. Different nationalities have certain characteristics. They also have certain problems that are peculiar to their race. We inherit many things from our parents. These can be either good or bad. Did you know that we can inherit certain types of bodies and the structure of our nervous system? Some people are more tense in their muscle structure. Some have muscles that are overly relaxed. This is known as the "flaccid muscle type."

Some curses are passed down through the generations. We inherit certain types of bodies which are predisposed to diabetes or they have poor eyesight or hearing. They have nerve problems. They inherit certain things like scoliosis of the spine. When this occurs, you should bind Satan by the power of the Holy Spirit and command the inherited physical, spiritual or emotional spirits to come out in the Name of Jesus.

Also, we should realize that when certain problems or diseases run in our family we should avoid aggravating these problems. For example, if your mother had diabetes, you would be foolish to eat a lot of carbohydrate foods, or foods containing a lot of starch or sugar. You are inviting that very infliction to come into your life.

Of course, we do inherit good things, too. One example would be that some people have a pelvis which enables them to walk all day and never get tired. A fellow in Green Bay, Wisconsin, who used to read water meters, could run up and down the steps of each house. Nobody in the town could do that. The man would work that way eight to ten hours and never get tired because of his pelvis.

In the Olympic games in Tokyo several years ago, there was a young man from the Dakotas who had lost his grandfather (he lived with his grandparents). He was so grieved that he just took to the hills and he ran and ran and he was getting himself in a strong physical shape. His pelvic structure was one which enhanced his ability for long distance running. He won two gold medals in the Tokyo Olympics.

Other people have a pelvis which is a little bit turned in, which causes them to be just a little bit pigeon-toed. This enables them to run very fast. These people would tire running a long-distance race. However, they are hard to beat when running short races.

People who for generations have farmed vegetable fields, bending over all day long, may never get tired of doing that because it is a natural thing for them to do. Some are at ease sitting on their heels. They can sit on their heels all day long. That's the natural way for them due to the position of their pelvis. So, it isn't necessary to feel bad because you can't sit on your heels or run twenty miles. You have a pelvis with which you are born. What is naturally easy for you may not be for another.

It is important to never be envious of another because you have something that they don't have and they have something that you don't have. God made us and we are each unique.

I think that one of the best things I have learned is that when I became a Christian, I received power over Satan. We can bind Satan and his control over our lives or the life of someone else by the power of the Holy Spirit in the Name

60

of Jesus. That enables us to free people from the demons which control them.

We should remember that what we hear, what we think, and the way we act can determine our success and happiness in our life, mentally physically and spiritually. But we are responsible to get rid of bad and negative attitudes or habits ourselves. God will help us but we must rid ourselves of the harmful attitudes and we must replace them with God's attitudes. God is at work within His children, helping us want to please Him, and then helping us do what He wants us to do (from Philippians 2:13 TLB).

Lack Of Education

Some people say that they suffer from a lack of education. They feel they are not worthy of whatever they might have. Although there might be things in their life over which they have no control, they, in Christ, can change their circumstances. We are children of God and do not need to feel inferior to anyone. God isn't!

Loneliness

Another thing that is of importance is to belong to a good Christian fellowship. If a person has been having a rough time in life, we need to inquire about them. Call them on the phone or visit them and talk to them. Encourage them. Many people don't want you to tell them what to do, they just want you to listen to them, and that is when we should listen to them. We need to learn to be good listeners. You would be surprised how much better people feel when they get something off their mind and just tell somebody about it.

People often blame Satan for all their problems. But, it is not always Satan causing their problems. If you go out in sub-zero temperatures without proper clothing, you might well get pneumonia or slip on ice and break a bone. Satan has not caused this problem. Your improper care of yourself was the cause. Sometimes in our lives, we lack good common sense. We do things which we just should not do, get ourselves into a bind and have a hard time getting out. It is not good to be alone, having no one to share with or to make suggestions or to encourage us.

Negativism

Negativism is an attitude which is drawn to the problems rather than to the solutions. Praise God for what He has done for you. Accentuate the improvement instead of the small portion of the problem remaining. God wants us healthy. The Word of God says, "My son, attend to my words; consent and submit to my sayings. Let them not depart from your sight; keep them in the center of your heart. For they are life to those who find them, healing and health to all their flesh" (Proverbs 4:20-22 Amp).

Overexposure

Our environment can be challenging to our health. Even sun exposure is causing skin problems and cancer for some individuals. Loud music may damage our eardrums. Overexposure to negative words, feelings and life-styles can be detrimental. What we hear, what we think about and the way we act will determine our success and happiness in our life in both mental and spiritual areas.

Poverty Syndrome

Some people have a poverty syndrome in their life. They think they have to be poor, that they are supposed to be that way. The Lord didn't make us that way. He wants us to prosper and be in health, even as our soul prospers.

Sleeplessness

Some people suffer from worry or overwork. They have a "sleep debt." They don't have enough sleep in their body. They are mentally fatigued. They suffer from chronic fatigue. They have headaches and stiffness in their bodies. They may also have stiffness in the joints of their feet, in their ankles and in their hands.

Wrong Living

When people let lusts rule them, they lose control. They may lust for money, prestige, power, sex, clothes, fancy cars or homes, foods, etc. It can be a lot of things. Too much a certain things will lead to sickness. Many times people are overindulging in caffeine, sugar, chemicals in food or preservatives.

We can change things

Although these examples are just a few of the many things which can block the receiving of a healing, many of these things we can change once we are aware they need to be changed. We do have control over a lot of things. For example, we can control our wrong living. We can say, "NO" to the lust for things that we don't need. We can change neighborhoods, friends, eating habits, etc.

It is true that people may suffer from lack of friendship and love; however, it is important to remember if the people in your life are a negative influence on you and drain you all the time, they don't really care about you. When someone cares for you, they will encourage you and help you. They will be a blessing in your life. Choose your friends carefully. And give friendship, love and blessings. What you give in God's laws will return to you, whether it is a smile, a helping hand, or healing. Freely you have received, freely give.

CHAPTER ELEVEN

Unforgiveness-A Hindrance To Healing

Norma Jean has such a wonderful teaching and testimony, she will share her experience in this chapter, trusting it will be a great blessing to our readers.

Christians usually don't have a problem getting along with God because they know they are the children of God and they know that He is the supreme Being. However, at times, they do experience trouble with each other. The Church is a family, and just like individual families, the children don't always get along really well with their brothers and sisters. Often they will quarrel.

"And whenever you stand praying, if you have anything against any one, forgive him and let it drop..." (Mark 11:25 & 26 Amp). That means let it drop; let it drop right down there to the ground, let it drop all the way. "(Leave it, let it go)..." If you drop something and you leave it, then you go away and you don't have it any more, do you?

"In order that your Father Who is in heaven may also forgive you your [own] failings and shortcomings, let them drop."

If you want God to forgive you and let your sins and failures be forgiven and dropped, then you have to do the same.

In Mark 11:26 it says, "But if you do not forgive, neither will your Father in heaven forgive your failings and shortcomings."

If we can't get along with each other on earth, how can we ever expect to get along with each other in heaven?

Sometimes we even wonder if people want to get to heaven. If I'm upset with you and I don't even want to be around you or see you, will one of us fail to get to heaven? Or, think about it, what are you going to do if the other person goes to heaven, are you going to stay here? If you go to heaven, is the other person going to stay here? However, if you want to be forgiven, you must forgive!

Not only that, unforgiveness can affect your life, in case you didn't know it (you probably do) it can affect your health, your happiness, your joy, your spiritual life and your peace. What is it worth to you to have peace? Many people never know one minute's peace. Some of them have plenty of money, but they cannot buy peace with it. A saying I like very much is "KNOW God and KNOW peace, NO God and NO peace."

The Bible teaches that if you don't forgive, you will not be forgiven. So remember, if you don't forgive, you are incapable of receiving forgiveness. In my past, I had never received love and I didn't know how to give love. If you have never received love, you will not know how to give love. Unforgiveness will keep you out of heaven. That is a fact! It will certainly hinder your prayers. Also, you cannot be free to forgive unless you have first forgiven yourself. Often, when you are having a problem, the first person you need to forgive is yourself. We tend--a lot of us--to just beat ourselves and place all the blame on ourselves.

Healing may be affected by unforgiveness. Unless you forgive, you cannot be assured of healing. Doctors have said that eighty-five percent of those hospitalized are suffering illnesses which are caused by resentment, bitterness, hate, revenge and anger; all of which have their roots in bitterness and unforgiveness. Most of these people could be dismissed if they could just get their emotions straightened out.

There are some people who have psychosomatic sicknesses and they do not really desire to be healed. They enjoy talking about and living with their sicknesses. You can make a decision to forgive and daily practice forgiveness. I can remember when I didn't know how to give or receive love. Someone prayed for me to have the baptism of love, and after that, I began to put my arms around people and start hugging them. At first, my arms felt so heavy I could hardly lift them, but I kept on hugging and soon it became very natural.

The following are a few illnesses which can come on as a result of envy, bitterness, anger, unforgiveness, etc.: Arthritis, high blood pressure, heart attacks and other heart problems, colitis, ulcers and other diseases.

Frances Hunter, at one of her meetings, shared a story about a woman whose finger was crippled with arthritis because she was always pointing her finger at others and telling them their faults. When this woman prayed the prayer of forgiveness with Frances, her finger straightened out.

Many people are living ruined lives because of unforgiveness. Jobs are lost because of unforgiveness because they cannot even get along with those with whom they work. Some heart problems are due to the adrenal glands over-producing when a person is constantly in a state of anger.

If you were chased by a dog, you might run a block or two and the adrenalin is used up; but when you stay angry or mad all the time, the adrenalin stays in your system, as previously mentioned, settles in your joints, resulting in arthritis. Remember, not every single case of arthritis is caused by unforgiveness, but it can certainly be a major factor for many.

Did you know that when you fail to forgive someone, you are just as though you were in a prison? They are holding you hostage and yet they may not even know that you are mad at them. They may be out dining and having a wonderful time and enjoying life and not being bothered, but you are busy trying to avoid them. When you see them, you may even go out of your way not to encounter them. You may not be able to eat and sleep because you are upset, and you become the slave to them because of your own unforgiveness. This, of course, is no way to live. Who wants to live that way?

My first husband, Wally Van Dell, and I experienced receiving the baptism with the Holy Spirit with several others. We ended up leaving our church because someone who did not have the same experience froze us out. One couple, who were our long-time friends, began avoiding us. Wally went up to them and asked them if we had done something to offend them and if we had, would they forgive us. Their answer was that someone from the church had told them that we were saying things about them that were not true. We had not seen nor talked to the ones who were talking about us. When we told our friends that, our friendship was restored.

I believe the best thing to do when you are aware of a coolness between friends is to just go up to them and say, "I feel I may have done something to offend you. If so, I'm sorry, will you forgive me?" That will give them an opportunity to respond, and hopefully the friendship can be mended.

Our actions sometimes may cause people to make wrong assumptions. You may run past a friend when in a hurry and not speak, or you may be concentrating on something and not notice someone. The best thing to do is to approach the person, apologize and save the friendship.

This happened to me one day while we were in Florida. I was on my way into the office where we had parked our trailer, and I dashed past a neighbor whom I knew well and didn't even acknowledge her. Immediately, the Spirit of God stopped me and I whirled around and told her that I was sorry. I had passed her up because my mind was so busy. She said, "I wondered what was wrong." We laughed and everything was all right, but if I had not stopped and apologized, a friendship could have ended.

What is our joy worth? Have you ever heard of anyone who has burst a blood vessel or even died in a fit of anger? Is anger or unforgiveness worth it? Lost joy can be likened to a clogged pipe in your home. Someone has to plunge or clear the line in some way. Unforgiveness and being judgmental is like the debris that clogs the drain. It is a blockage that affects our spiritual life. Luke 6:37 (Amp) says, "Judge not [neither pronouncing judgment nor subjecting to censure], and you will not be judged; do not condemn and pronounce guilty, and you will not be condemned and pronounced guilty; acquit and forgive and release, (give up resentment, let it drop)..."

There you go, let it drop. Get rid of it completely, let it drop. "And you will be acquitted and forgiven and released." That is exactly what we need to do.

God says, "Vengeance is mine." When I was a widow, I bought a Suburban. It said right on it 9,857 miles. I happened to know the man who owned it before. I even called him and asked him if that was the true mileage because usually you wouldn't sell it that soon. He assured me that it was correct. I reminded him that Wally had died and I was a widow and that I would have to pull the trailer with this vehicle alone. I said to him if he said I shouldn't buy it, I would never say a word why and I wouldn't buy it. He again assured me it was good. I bought it and had nothing but troubles with it. I made one trip to Florida and back, putting thousands of dollars into the thing for repairs. I really didn't have that kind of money to spend since I was a widow. I was so poor, even the mice would sit in the corner and cry! (I was broker than the Ten Commandments!) I finally had to get rid of that vehicle.

My son found a new Suburban and in the process of trading, they discovered that the used Suburban I had purchased had 109,857 miles on it before I purchased it. The dealer had gypped me, and I had warned him what would happen to him if he cheated me (a widow) and how God would take care of him. He lied! I could have really held a grudge against him. I could have sued him because I had proof that the mileage had 109,857 miles.

However, I had to think about what my joy was worth. I was out on the road as an evangelist. I couldn't be tied down in Minneapolis with a lawsuit. I considered how that would affect my ministry and how could I tell others how to live if I was busy suing someone. God had been faithful in answering my prayers each month and provided the money for the repairs. The Bible tells us we can have favor with those with whom we would ordinarily not have favor and that is why I knew God would take care of that car dealer. It didn't pay for him to do that. By the next time I came up north, he was out of business.

Many couples have problems over little things, such as pointing out one another's faults. One squeezes the toothpaste in the middle or leaves the towels disarrayed. The other will get so angry. Is losing your joy over something so trivial worth it? Is it worth losing your joy because you are nursing a grudge and being mad? Of course, the answer is "no" and these things can block you from receiving your healing. If we are mad with one another or full of anger, we are not able to have our minds stayed on Christ, which is vitally important to enable us to live in the world. If we are unforgiving, we can lose our health, we can be robbed of our joy, peace of mind and even our very life.

How are we to forgive? Jesus told Peter to forgive seven times seventy. That's 490 times. Could it be that Jesus was telling us to keep count and when we get up 490 times we could quit forgiving? I imagine Jesus figured by the time we forgave 490 times, we would be in such a habit of forgiving that we would continue to forgive.

Ephesians 4:31 & 32 (Amp) says, "Let all bitterness and indignation and wrath (passion, rage, bad temper) and resentment (anger, animosity) and quarreling (brawling, clamor, contention) and slander (evilspeaking, abusive or blasphemous language) be banished from you..." Well, that covers just about all the faults we can have, doesn't it? "With all malice (spite, ill will or baseness of any kind)." Now, this is what you are supposed to do instead of those bad things: "And become useful and helpful and kind to one another, tenderhearted (compassionate, understanding, lovinghearted), forgiving one another [readily and freely], as God in Christ forgave you" (verse 32). That sounds to me like a command as to how we are supposed to live.

We cannot go around with all those things in our hearts and still have the love of Jesus toward each other. You can even hold up the salvation of another, even a loved one, with your unforgiveness. When my son, Greg, was in high school, he had evidently started drinking. Although I didn't realize it, he went on to college and was expelled in less than six months for drinking. He became an alcoholic and went on to using and dealing drugs. This kid gave me such a pain in the neck! At this time, I was in the hospital bed at home (before I was healed). He would even break into our home and take my sleeping pills and pain pills. We had to have the locks on the doors changed four times to try to keep him out. Throughout this time, he almost drove me crazy. He did everything he could to vex and torment me. I was trying to operate a tax business from my hospital bed and Greg would tie up the phone for hours, which is very important during the three months of tax season. I would end up so distraught that I did not know what to do.

I reached the point that I wished I would never see him again. Sometimes, I would not hear from him for a year or more and that would be a happier time than when he was around. Obviously, I wasn't Spirit-filled (with God's Spirit) at the time, I was mad-filled. I would even put a taped message of salvation on the phone until he would hang up rather than listen to it. I believed that the less I would see him, the happier I would be.

But you cannot forget that easily a son you brought into the world.

Greg was naturally gifted musically. He played trombone and accordion after lessons on them and he played every other musical instrument by ear. He was Minnesota's top trombonist in his senior year. He played drums, 12-string guitar, bass guitar, bass drum, the whole works. He was so talented musically; yet, he hocked every one of those instruments for drug money. He went down to the bottom, but we prayed for him night and day, night and day.

After I was healed, Wally and I went to the Institute of Ministry in Florida. We sat under teachings on unforgiveness. Naturally, that hit me right in the head. I felt I was justified in my feelings toward Greg as he was the one who had wronged me, but I found out at the Institute of Ministry that it didn't matter who was the one wronged or the one doing wrong. I was still to forgive.

We went home a couple of days before Christmas and Greg called us on Christmas Eve. He would always spend all his time telling me how the psychiatrists, psychologists and everyone told him that everything was my fault. If it wasn't for me, he would be okay. That night, I let him say all he had stored up for awhile.

When he got all through, I said, "Greg, I guess you're right. For what I didn't know about raising kids and the money we didn't have and the health that I didn't have, I just did the best I could, and I guess it wasn't good enough and I'm sorry. Will you forgive me?"

You should have seen him turn around about 360 degrees and start telling me how good I was! The following year, he came to one of our meetings. He put a dollar in the offering. He wasn't saved yet, and we found out later that it was the last dollar he had. He ended up coming out to the house, and he said he had been off drugs for a certain amount of time. We told him that was good.

He talked about how much we had changed. Of course, when they have been away and come back, they always tell you how much you have changed. Greg is 6'6" and I'm about 5'1" and when I went out to the kitchen and he followed me and draped his arms around me and told me that he had been mean and rotten to me most of his life and that he was sorry and asked me to forgive him, I told him I already had.

He let me know he really loved me. Things gradually changed.

Greg went through a treatment program and got off drugs. Back and forth he wavered for awhile as he went through treatment four times. When I brought Wally home from Florida the year he died, Greg came out of treatment and visited his Dad. That was his last time in treatment, and he spent all the time after his Dad died trying to make up to me for all the wrong he had done. He just couldn't do enough. He got married, came back to church and got saved. To this day, he continues to go to church and Sunday School. He also is involved with the choir and attends men's prayer breakfasts and reads the Bible each morning before going to work.

I never thought I would see the day when he would be like that. He even installed a $3,000 phone system in the Kansas City Rescue Mission at no cost to them and has gone out on the streets collecting funds for them. I even sent him his Dad's preaching Bible with the notes in it, which is so special to him.

Now, he asks me for prayer and advice. Following is a portion of a letter Greg wrote to me in 1990 that I would like to share with you:
"Mom,

I know you tend to beat yourself by saying you don't feel that you're a good mother. Don't do that. You took us to church, you taught us to fear God, fed us like no one else ever will (he figures I'm a good cook!) and prayed unceasingly for our salvation. God has a beautiful crown for you. I only pray I can do half as well as you."

I cried when I read that. He asked me to tell everybody wherever I go to never quit praying for their children. He said that if his Dad and I and Dr. Le Roy had ever quit praying for him, he would not be where he is today.

All of this has come about since I said, "I'm sorry, will you forgive me?" I said this even though he was the one who had given me a pain in the neck most of his life. If I had not done that, I don't believe he would have ever been saved or any of this would have ever come around.

John 20:23 (Amp) says, "[Now, having received the Holy Spirit and being led and directed by Him] if you forgive the sins of any one, they are forgiven; and if you retain the sins of any one, they are retained."

I had to forgive a lot of the past. Greg did so many things, many of which I never even knew. I knew he was in and out of jail and different things like that, but I never knew how bad everything was and he says he's never going to tell me. That's fine with me. I don't even want to know because what's past is past.

The Bible doesn't say to forgive only those we wrong. It says to forgive whether we did the wrong or they did the wrong.

There was a time when I just hated Greg, but I can say now that I love that kid (although he is 6'6", as I previously mentioned, grown and married with his own family, to me, he will always be "my kid"), and I could not be more proud of him. We truly have come a long way.

No matter what we have against someone, we must forgive them. At one of the meetings with Charles and Frances Hunter, a lady came to the microphone and said that she forgave the men who murdered her son.

How many of us are holding unforgiveness for a much lesser offense? Colossians 3:13 gives us a type of recipe for forgiveness. We are not supposed to hold grudges and be unforgiving. We are supposed to forgive as the Lord forgave us. Colossians 3:13 (Amp) says, "Be gentle and forbearing with one another and, if one has a difference (a grievance or complaint) against another, readily pardoning each other; even as the Lord has freely forgiven you, so must you also forgive."

In the Living Bible this verse says, "Be gentle and ready to forgive; never hold grudges. Remember, the Lord forgave you, so you must forgive others." That's a good recipe. Also, it is an order, not a choice. God's Word shows us our part, and He is always faithful to do His part.

One thing I would like to caution you about is that there are cases when it may be best to just forgive someone to God and ask God to forgive those who hurt you. For instance, I had a lot of unforgiveness against my mother that I had to get rid of when I went into the ministry.

My mother raised me telling me I was dumb, homely and bad shaped, and she wished that she had drowned me when I was little. I didn't have good feelings toward my mother. I was always criticized and beaten until I left home at the age of fifteen. Although my Dad was fairly good to me, he turned against me when I went into the ministry.

So, I had to go through this act of forgiveness with both parents. But, I didn't dare go up to my mother and say, "I forgive you for the way you treated me all those years" because that would just open up a can of worms. If it is something like that and they don't know you have any unforgiveness and it is only one-sided, then I recommend that you don't go to them. Just ask God to forgive them and tell God that you forgive them.

Christ forgave from an old rugged cross, and if He could do that, I guess we can at least forgive one another. God is calling each of us to forgiveness. Ask him to show you anyone you need to forgive. Following is a prayer I hope you will pray:

God, I ask You to forgive me for having unforgiveness in my heart. I don't want to be unforgiving. I renounce all spirits of hate, bitterness, revenge, envy, resentment, anger and unforgiveness. Jesus, I ask You to fill me with love, joy and peace. And, now, dear Jesus, I want to forgive (put in the names or relationships of all those you need to forgive, such as mother, father, friends' names, etc.) God, I ask You to use Your Holy Spirit eraser to erase every memory of any and all past unforgiveness. Cleanse all hurts and wounds and fill me with forgiveness toward everyone. Help me, dear Jesus, to live each day in such a way that people will see You living in me. Thank You for doing this. Thank You for forgiving me. I now receive Your forgiveness. In Jesus' Name. Amen."

Now, if you need healing and you have prayed this prayer, you are free from the hindrance of unforgiveness and you can expect to receive your healing.

CHAPTER TWELVE

In His Service

Norma Jean and I thank you for the opportunity to minister to you through this book on "The Supernatural Spine." We live to serve God and although we have given up most of what we had (both of us gave up our businesses and homes), we are blessed with a wonderful trailer that we live in year-round. We travel around the country ministering in the Name of the Lord Jesus Christ.

Many say, "You need a house--some place to call home, a place to put your roots down." But we are happy serving the Lord wherever He leads us. To us, wherever the trailer is parked at any one time is home. That's what keeps us young! May God bless you.

If you would like to have us minister to your group or at your church, please write us.

Impossible Miracles Ministry
549 Manor Drive, N.E.
Minneapolis, MN 55432

Closing Blessing

In closing, we suggest to you that Psalm 103 is very good to read to someone who is very depressed in their life, or having a nervous breakdown, or whatever the problem. Psalm 103 is a good Psalm to read, because David said, "Bless the Lord, O my soul: and all that is within me, bless his holy name." We must learn to bless each other.

Norma Jean and I bless each other every morning. Just place your right hand on the person's forehead and bless them with whatever you wish them to have. To have a good day, to be blessed in their work, etc.

Bless your children as they go off to school that they will learn much and get good marks.

Wives, bless your husbands as they go off to work, and husbands, bless your wives as they partake in whatever they are doing. And, we should never forget, we are blessed to be a blessing in the Name of Jesus.

And here is our blessing for you:

"That the the Lord will bless you, that you will do all you can to serve Him and do the things that please Him. That you will think on things that are pure and holy." Our verse for you is III John 2, "Beloved, I wish above all things that thou mayest prosper and be in health, even as thy soul prospereth."

Remember that God said to Abraham, "If you will believe, you will be blessed, and I will bless you if you do this or bless you if you do that."

There's a big "if" there. If we do what God tells us to do, He will bless us. If we don't, then, of course, we all know the results. May you be blessed all the days of your life. We bless you in Jesus' Name.

Exercises To Strengthen The Lower Back

***Important Note: Consult your physician before beginning any exercise program.**

There are some special exercises which we would like to encourage you to do. These will help you strengthen the muscles associated with your lower back. It is extremely important that these muscles be in proper position and of proper strength. If one muscle is weaker than another, your vertebrae will tend to pull to the side of the strong muscle. This most likely would result in an obstruction to the signals sent out to the various organs through the nerves going out from the spinal column. The end result will be that the organ will not function properly as it is dependent upon operational signals sent to it from the brain, through the nerves. Also, blood vessels may be obstructed affecting the health of an organ and causing it to function improperly.

Fig. 1 - *Lying on your back, both hands behind your left knee, push your leg down and hold back with your hands. Count to four while holding your leg. Repeat 3 times.*

Fig. 2 - *Put both hands behind your right knee, push your leg down and hold back with your hands. Count to four while holding your leg. Repeat 3 times.*

Fig. 3 - *Put both hands behind both legs, push legs down and resist with your hands. Count to four while holding your legs. Repeat 3 times.*

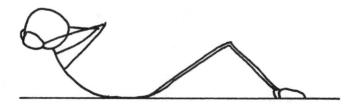

Fig. 4 - *Laying on your back, hands behind your head and knees bent, pull your head and shoulders up and hold. Count to four, relax and repeat 3 times.*

Fig. 5 - *Laying on your back, hands behind your head, raise your legs about three inches off the floor and hold them up as you count to four. Repeat 3 times. (This exercise will strengthen the abdominal muscles and also the lumbar muscles because they work together.)*

Always remember when you start out, only do an exercise a few times, gradually building up the number of times you do the exercise. This will help you develop the muscles by gently stretching them and not strain the muscles, ligaments and tendons.

It will take you about three weeks of exercising (four to five times a week) before you will notice any difference in your back being strengthened. You will also notice that your abdominal muscles will become stronger.

Norma Jean Van Dell, after 31 hospital visits, 10 operations and 100% permanent disability was made whole by one touch from the Master and has never been the same since. She and her husband Wally began the "Impossible Miracles Ministry." On June 28, 1981, Wally went to be with the Lord. Norma Jean continued with the ministry, pulling her trailer around the country wherever God called her. God honored her faithfulness and met her needs.

Dr. Roy J. Le Roy is a chiropractor who prays for his patients. While he and his wife Florence attended the Institute of Ministry in Bradenton, Florida, Florence went to be with the Lord on March 6, 1982. He continued this pastoral training school in the winter, returning to his practice in Green Bay, Wisconsin, each Spring. During this time, he and Norma Jean shared their mutual grief and loneliness.

In January, 1984, when Dr. Le Roy returned to Florida, a spark was kindled and God brought two lonely people together. They were married on March 11, 1984, in Florida and together they continue with the "Impossible Miracles Ministry." God is moving mightily in their ministry as Dr. Le Roy teaches on "How To Minister Healing To Yourself And Others" and Norma Jean shares her testimony.